£4.99
UK only

# Annual 1996

## THE BATMAN ADVENTURES

Based on the smash hit cartoon: Batman: The Animated Series!

This book is sold subject to the condition that it shall not, by way of trade or otherwise, be lent, resold, hired out or otherwise circulated without the publisher's prior consent in any form of binding or cover other than that in which this is published and without similar condition being imposed on the subsequent purchaser.

Published in Great Britain by World International, an imprint of Egmont Publishing Ltd., Egmont House, PO Box 111, Great Ducie Street, Manchester M60 3BL

Printed in Italy

ISBN: O-7498-2316-X

Batman and all related indicia are trademarks of DC Comics ©1995. All Rights Reserved.

The stories, characters and names featured in this publication are the property of DC Comics and are used under licence from DC Comics.

Batman created by Bob Kane.

Origination by Newsstand Services
Compilation Editor: James Hill
Package Design: Rob Sharp
Cover Art: Dev Madan

## Contents

**THE EYES OF JUSTICE ARE WATCHING**

**G**otham City. It is often a gloomy, shadowy city; a sometimes dangerous place filled with hidden terrors and unseen evils. Gotham...where, as a young boy, Bruce Wayne saw his parents fall victim to a senseless crime and vowed to avenge their deaths. After years of study and practice, he donned the costume of the Batman and now strikes fear into the hearts of the city's criminals. Gotham... where terrors no longer remain hidden, evils unseen. Gotham... where from deep within the shadows of the Bat...

*...the eyes of justice are watching!*

# GOOD FACE BAD FACE

Copyright ©1994 DC Comics Inc.

KELLEY PUCKETT — WRITER   MIKE PAROBECK — PENCILS   RICK B. — INKS   RICK T. — COLORS   RICK S. — LETTERS   DARREN VINCENZO — ASST. EDITOR   SCOTT PETERSON — EDITOR   BATMAN CREATED BY BOB KANE

"...HATRED OF ONE RUPERT THORNE, ALONG WITH THE STRESS OF THE EVENTS LEADING UP TO THE PATIENT'S DISFIGUREMENT, CAUSED "BIG, BAD HARV," AN ALTER-EGO PERSONA CREATED BY YEARS OF REPRESSED ANGER, TO MANIFEST WITH GREATER FREQUENCY..."

"...BELIEVE THAT "HARVEY" INTERPRETED HIS SCARRING AS AN EXTERNAL REPRESENTATION OF THE DARK SIDE HE'D HIDDEN FOR SO LONG. THE SHOCK OF THIS TRANSFORMATION WAS TOO MUCH FOR "HARVEY," AND THAT PERSONA SUBMERGED, LEAVING "BIG, BAD HARV" IN CONTROL..."

"...DEPENDENCY ON THE COIN FOR ALL SIGNIFICANT DECISIONS STILL PUZZLES ME. WHEN QUESTIONED, HE TALKS OF THE RANDOM-NESS OF LIFE, OF CHANCE -- YET I SEE NO CONNECTION..."

"...NOW BEGIN TO REFER TO THE PATIENT'S DOMINANT PERSONA AS "TWO-FACE." "BIG BAD HARV," LITTLE MORE THAN A SIMPLE EXPRESSION OF RAGE, HAS CHANGED OVER THE PAST SEVERAL MONTHS INTO A FRIGHTENINGLY CAPABLE, LOGICAL, UNIQUE PERSONA..."

THERE, THAT'S BET--

YIKES!

STAY CALM. I'M HERE TO HELP.

THE CELL DOORS ARE ELECTRONICALLY CONTROLLED -- HOW DO YOU KEEP THEM LOCKED WHEN THE POWER'S CUT?

AAA... AAA... ALTERNATE G·GENERATOR. POWERS THE DOORS. KEEPS 'EM SHUT.

SO THERE'S NO WAY TO OPEN THEM UNTIL FULL POWER'S RESTORED.

RIGHT. WELL, UNLESS YOU DID IT FROM THE SECONDARY CONTROL ROOM.

"SECONDARY..?"

13

# Adventures in Animation

## Batman's latest on-screen flight may be the most faithful yet...

Gotham's Dark Knight has been interpreted on film and television many times throughout his long history. In mid-1943, Columbia Pictures released *Batman*, a 15-chapter serial, and since then little time has passed without there being a new cinematic or televisual version of Batman to thrill and delight fans. Each version has taken the essential comic book elements and poured in new ingredients - Japanese spies in the War years, camp humour in the 1960s, grim cyberpunk in the dark movies of the 1990s - each time mixing a cocktail of visual imagery and stories perfectly suited to its era.

And what of the latest addition to this canon, *Batman: The Animated Series*? How best to describe it? The phrase *dark deco* has been coined to characterise the show's mix of thick shadows and angular architecture reminiscent of 1930s art deco. Films from that era such as *Citizen Kane*, are also an influence, evoking a shadowy mood that harks back to the earliest Batman comic strips as drawn by the character's creator, Bob Kane.

"There's many ways of doing Batman, as long as they're cool," revealed *Batman: The Animated Series* producer Bruce Timm in an interview in *Hero* magazine in 1993. "We feel *Batman: TAS* is one *right way* to do Batman."

Dark night - Gotham's nocturnal guardian swings into action

An explosive scene from *Batman: The Animated Series*

With a total of 85 episodes and a 70-minute film, *Mask of The Phantasm*, (released in the cinema in America and direct to video in the UK), *Batman: The Animated Series* is certainly a highly successful *right way* to do Batman. Work on the show began as early as 1990 when Bruce Timm and fellow producer, Eric Radomski, were asked to put together a Batman cartoon.

The pair first worked on a short promo piece, designed to show the style that would be used for the finished series. "I designed all the characters and did the storyboards (sequences of comic strip-like illustrations detailing the action to be filmed), while Eric did the background styling," remembered Timm in *Comics Scene* magazine in April 1993.

However, all did not go smoothly and it soon became apparent to Radomski that painting in all the black areas planned for the film would be very time consuming. Hitting upon an unusual solution, Radomski decided to airbrush the cartoon background on black paper - breaking an old animation 'rule' that requires cartoons to be drawn on white paper. Timm was worried that the effect would look dull, but his fears were groundless and the sombre tone of the promo short set the feel for the entire series.

With the two minute promotional film meeting a favourable response, (eventually forming the basis of the show's title sequence), Timm and Radomski soon found themselves as executive producers for the first time. Joined by co-producer Alan Burnett (and later, head writer/executive producer Paul Dini), they headed up a full team of writers, model artists, storyboard artists, directors, voice actors and animators who worked round the clock to create the series.

The three producers were not only familiar with Batman, but had been fans of the comic series for many years and so inspiration was easy to find. It took Bruce Timm barely an hour to come up with the drawings that would eventually become the main character designs for the Dark Knight in *Batman: The Animated Series*. Other characters followed, including Bruce Wayne, Two-Face, Clayface and Batgirl. When asked by *Comics Scene* about who was responsible for the show's vision, Timm had a definite answer. "It's mostly Eric Radomski's and my vision of the show," he said, "and Alan Burnett's, as well. It really is a split three-way collaboration."

However, though Timm designed Batman the way "I always wanted to see Batman look", the clean illustrative style resembles that used by the first Batman comic book artists of the 1930s and 1940s. This simplicity is, according to Timm, the key to successful animation. "The more detail you have on a character the harder it is for that character to move," he explained in *Comics Scene*.

**D**ramatic storyboards by Bruce Timm from the *Batman: The Animated Series* episode, Laughing Fish

ACTION BATMAN'S P.O.V. JOKER WHIRLS AROUND.

ACTION JOKER'S P.O.V. BATMAN ANTICS BACK

The writers for *Batman: The Animated Series*, (many of them experienced Batman comic writers), also took much from the strips, most notably Batman's bizarre rogues' gallery. Batman's arch foes were faithfully recreated - the Joker remained a theatrical madman, Catwoman an expert cat thief with an undeniable attraction to Batman, and Poison Ivy a cruel manipulator of men.

"When I came on (the show), I started tracking down comic book writers as fast as I could," revealed Alan Burnett, also speaking in *Comics Scene* magazine in 1992. "I gathered people who love Batman and they've taken the show places I couldn't have gone without them." In fact, the show has gone on to win an Emmy, the television equivalent of an Oscar, for Best Writing in an Animated Series.

However, an essential way in which *Batman: The Animated Series* breaks free from its comic book roots is in its use of words and pictures to tell a story. Though visual in nature, comics are essentially static and often have to rely on dialogue balloons and caption boxes to relate mood and essential story information. Cartoons, at their best, are anything but static. "Bruce (Timm) and I always felt...completely separate from each other...that cartoons are way too chatty," asserted Eric Radomski in his *Comics Scene* interview. "You don't need Batman talking throughout the whole episode. It's more interesting for him to walk into a darkened room, open up a file and let the audience read it, than for him to go, 'Hmmm, I wonder what's in that file cabinet?'"

Alan Burnett agrees. "We're not afraid to do silence," he told *Comic World* magazine in March 1994. A sentiment shared by Bruce Timm who in *Hero* magazine announced, "Timing is a very important part of our

Dark Deco - the moody style of Batman's latest TV incarnation

show. It's not like most other adventure cartoons where everything is moving at the same speed. In them, when two characters are speaking the lines are falling on top of each other - there's no *dramatic pauses*."

Drama is certainly not something *Batman: The Animated Series* is short on. It remains faithful to the current style of Batman's comic adventures while at the same time it mixes in elements from the strip's earliest days, creating a feel all of its own - one that is simultaneously familiar and dazzlingly original. It is perhaps the perfect adaptation, taking material direct from the source and reworking it for a entirely different medium. And, as such, it is bound to endure the test of time and engage Batman fans for many years to come.

Popular comic character, Man-Bat made an appearance in the TV episode, *On Leather Wings*

Paws for thought - Batman and Catwoman are locked in a love/hate relationship

THE JOKER in LAUGHTER AFTER MIDNIGHT

PAUL DINI — JOHN BYRNE
WRITER — PENCILLER

RICK BURCHETT INKER

BRUCE TIMM — STARKINGS/COMICRAFT
COLORIST — LETTERING

DARREN VINCENZO — SCOTT PETERSON
ASST. ED. — EDITOR

IT'S OKAY, DON'T GET UP. I'M FINE.

THROW ME OUT OF A POLICE BLIMP, WILL YOU? WHY, I OUGHTA....

1

Copyright ©1994 DC Comics Inc.

THE
POISON.

NOW.

"...I DON'T THINK YOU'LL HAVE TO WORRY ABOUT SEEING ACACHIANO POISON IN GOTHAM AGAIN."

THE END?